RSPCA

Lamb All Alone

The Royal Society for the Prevention of Cruelty to Animals is the UK's largest animal charity. They rescue, look after and rehome hundreds of thousands of animals each year in England and Wales. They also offer advice on caring for all animals and campaign to change laws that will protect them. Their work relies on your support, and buying this book helps them save animals' lives.

www.rspca.org.uk

Lamb
All Alone

By Kate Davies
Illustrated by Jon Davis

SCHOLASTIC

First published in the UK in 2013 by Scholastic Children's Books
An imprint of Scholastic Ltd
Euston House, 24 Eversholt Street
London, NW1 1DB, UK
Registered office: Westfield Road, Southam, Warwickshire, CV47 0RA
SCHOLASTIC and associated logos are trademarks
and/or registered trademarks of Scholastic Inc.

Text copyright © RSPCA, 2013
Illustration copyright © RSPCA, 2013

ISBN 978 1407 13323 2

RSPCA name and logo are trademarks of RSPCA used by
Scholastic Ltd under license from RSPCA Trading Ltd.
Scholastic will donate a minimum amount to the RSPCA from
every book sold. Such amount shall be paid to RSPCA Trading Limited
which pays all its taxable profits to the RSPCA. Registered in
England and Wales Charity No. 219099
www.rspca.org.uk

A CIP catalogue record for this book is available
from the British Library.

Printed and bound by CPI Group (UK) Ltd, Croydon, CR0 4YY
Papers used by Scholastic Children's Books are made
from wood grown in sustainable forests.

9 10 8

This is a work of fiction. Names, characters, places,
incidents and dialogues are products of the author's imagination
or are used fictitiously. Any resemblance to actual people,
living or dead, events or locales is entirely coincidental.

www.scholastic.co.uk

1

"Turn to page five in your maths books, everyone. . ."

Ben tried to concentrate on what Mrs Jackson was saying, but the gentle drumming of the rain against the window made him feel sleepy. It had been pouring non-stop for an entire week. *Surely the sky should have run out of water by now,* thought Ben.

It had been fun last Monday, when the rain started. He and his best friends, Tom and Sam, had walked to school in their wellington boots, splashing through

the puddles as they passed fields full of
sheep and newborn lambs. On Tuesday it
wasn't quite so fun – Tom had jumped in
a puddle, splashing water over the top of
Ben's wellies, and Ben had to sit through
a whole day of school in his stinky wet
socks. By Wednesday the sheep had
started looking very sorry for themselves,
their woolly coats heavy with water, and
Ben's mum decided she'd drive him to
school until the rain stopped. Ben didn't

like being in the car much – it smelled of sickly-sweet air freshener, and Mum always had the radio tuned into the news or classical music.

Now it was Monday again, and the rain *still* hadn't stopped. Ben had been cooped up inside all weekend. He'd missed football practice, the last one before the Easter holidays, and he'd played every computer game he had at least twice. Mum hadn't even let him walk his sheepdog, Jess, or go swimming with his eighteen-year-old sister, Kate, who had a weekend job as a lifeguard at the local pool. "I don't want you coming down with a cold," she'd said. Ben didn't think getting a cold would be so bad – at least then he could stay off school and not worry about long multiplication.

Ben started counting the raindrops chasing each other down the classroom windows, giving himself double points when they joined together into one big drop. He'd reached forty-four when he felt a sharp jab in his ribs.

"Ben!" Tom hissed, jerking his head towards Mrs Jackson. Ben looked round. The whole of 6J was staring at him – and so was his teacher.

"Did you hear what I just said, Ben?" asked Mrs Jackson, raising her eyebrows.

Ben looked at her blankly. "Er . . . yes?" he said – but he hadn't.

"Great!" she said. "Come up and write the answer on the board, then." She waggled the whiteboard pen at Ben.

He stood up as slowly as he could, desperately trying to remember what Mrs Jackson had been talking about. He looked at Tom and Sam but they just shrugged their shoulders. They obviously hadn't been listening, either. Ben walked to the front of the classroom, and took the whiteboard pen from Mrs Jackson. The sum on the board made no sense to him – the numbers just swam around in front of his eyes. He wrote the number "55" in big red letters. It was as good a guess as any.

"No, Ben. The answer's one hundred and seventy-six," said Mrs Jackson, rubbing out the sum. "But I don't think you were listening when I explained the question, were you?"

Ben shook his head, and Mrs Jackson smiled at him.

"I know it's miserable outside, but please try to pay attention instead of staring out of the window."

Ben nodded.

"Have a go at another one," said Mrs Jackson, turning back to the whiteboard. Her bracelets jangled as she wrote the new problem on the board.

"OK, Ben. What's seven times forty-eight?"

Just at that moment, there was a sharp *rat-tat-tat* at the classroom door. Mrs Jackson went to open it, and Ben dashed back to his seat.

"How lucky are you?" whispered Tom.

"I know! Let's hope she forgets about me," said Ben.

"Shh!" said Sam, pointing at the door. "It's Mr Hughes!"

Mr Hughes was their head teacher. Ben really liked him – he made brilliant jokes in assembly, and always joined in for the races on Sports Day – but today he wasn't smiling at all.

"Good morning, children," he said as he walked into the classroom. "I just need to have a quick word with Mrs Jackson. . ."

Mrs Jackson and Mr Hughes stood at the front of the room, talking in hushed voices, while the whole class whispered among themselves, trying to guess what was going on.

"Maybe they're going to give us all Easter eggs to make up for not being able to play outside!" said Ben hopefully. "Or a class pet! We've been asking for one for ages!"

"No way . . . it must be something bad," said Sam, straining to hear what the teachers were saying. "The last time Mr Hughes looked that serious was when the whole of year two came down with chickenpox."

"Maybe all the teachers have caught measles!"

"Maybe a killer bug has come from outer space!"

"Maybe an alien spaceship has landed in the playground!"

"Yeah, and maybe they're looking for ten-year-old boys to take back to their planet!" said Tom.

"They'll probably clone us, and then—" started Sam.

"Don't worry, boys – I just walked through the playground, and I didn't see any aliens," said Mr Hughes. Sam blushed, and Tom became very interested in a tiny mark on his desk.

"But I do have something to tell you all," Mr Hughes continued. "You'll probably have noticed that it's still raining. Well, the Environment Agency has issued a

flood warning for the area. They think the river is going to overflow – and if that happens, the school might be flooded."

Everyone started whispering to each other excitedly. Ben nudged Tom and grinned. Imagine . . . it would be even better than a snow day. They wouldn't have to do maths homework for weeks!

"Settle down, everyone," said Mr Hughes, holding up his hands to silence the class. "I haven't finished. Because of the risk of flooding, I'm afraid I've had to call your parents. They're all on their way to collect you – the school is closed until further notice."

"HOORAY!" A huge cheer went up around the classroom.

"Yesssss!" said Ben, punching the air. "No more long multiplication. I'm going home to play with Jess!"

"I'm going to watch TV for the rest of the day and eat fish fingers for tea," said Tom, packing up his pencil case.

Sam was the only one not smiling. "I really hope my bedroom isn't flooded," he said.

"Your bedroom's on the first floor!" said Ben, shaking his head. "The water will never get up there."

But that made Ben think – his bedroom

was on the ground floor, looking out on to the garden. He'd better hurry home and make sure all his things were safe.

2

"The Met Office has issued a severe flood warning for parts of southern England. . ." Ben sat in the front of the car, next to his mum. He was glued to every word the man on the radio said. For once, he didn't mind listening to the news – they were talking about where he lived . . . and his village might be flooded that afternoon!

Ben tapped his fingers on his knees impatiently. His mother was driving so slowly he might as well have been walking.

"Can't we go a bit faster, Mum?" Ben asked, looking out of the window. The heavy grey clouds were so low it looked as if they were almost touching the trees, and rain blurred the road ahead of them.

"I'm sorry, Ben – we can't risk getting stuck, or driving into the ditch. I can barely see the road!" She steered the car carefully, avoiding the deep puddles and the streams of water running through the gutter.

They drove past pretty thatched cottages, through the rows of shops in the middle of the village, and up the hill towards their house. Mum slowed down as they passed Mr Green's farm, and at last they were home. The warm red-brick house looked cosy and inviting, and Ben jumped out of the car and rushed for the shelter of the porch.

As Mum opened the front door Ben could hear Jess barking and racing up and down the hall. She jumped up at Ben as soon as he was inside, wagging her tail hopefully – he usually took her for a walk when he got back from school, when it wasn't pouring with rain.

"Sorry, girl," he said, rubbing her head. "We're not going anywhere for a while."

Ben and Mum had just taken off their coats when the front door opened again, and Kate staggered in. She looked as though someone had tipped a bucket of water over her head. Ben burst out laughing.

"Kate!" cried Mum. "You didn't walk to college in this weather, did you? I told you to get the bus."

"The buses weren't running," said Kate,

as Mum handed her a towel. "And it was a waste of time anyway. By the time I'd got there, they were sending everyone home. Have they shut Dad's office, too?"

"Not yet – but he's going to try and get home as early as he can," said Mum.

"He'll have to swim here at this rate," said Kate. "I might have to throw him a life jacket out the window."

Kate shook her head to dry herself off. Water from her hair sprayed all over the hall, and all over Ben.

"Hey!" he shouted. "You're worse than Jess."

Kate nudged Ben and he nudged her back.

"Come on, you two," said Mum, steering them towards the living room. "We don't have long to get the house ready in case it floods, so let's have all hands on deck. Kate, start taking the living-room chairs upstairs. Ben, start packing up your bedroom. Then you can help me roll up the rugs."

They jumped into action. Kate piled two small chairs on top of each other and carried them upstairs to her parents' bedroom.

Ben followed Kate up the stairs, carrying a rucksack full of his favourite books and DVDs. As he reached the top of the staircase he heard a deep, low

rumbling – thunder. A proper storm
was raging now.

Ben found Kate looking out of their
parents' bedroom window, her hands on
her hips. The sky had grown darker, and
lightning flashed down to the fields just
past the garden. Their house was one of
several scattered across the hills at the
edge of the village. Ben usually wished
he lived in the valley near the shops,

like Tom and Sam, but today he was really glad he lived up a hill — it would definitely be one of the last places to flood. The fields to the right were on even higher ground than the house, but just past the end of their garden, there was a grassy slope that led down to low-lying pastures.

The slope was beginning to look like a waterfall — it was hard to believe they'd been somersaulting down it in the sunshine a few weeks ago. As another bolt of lightning lit up the sky, the oak tree on the hill at the end of the field seemed to jump out at them, silhouetted in the storm like something from a horror story.

"Wow . . . look at that," said Kate. "And look how high the river is now," she said, pointing to it. It was several fields away, but they could still see how much higher it had become. Usually it was more like a gentle stream, but today it was definitely a river, and a powerful one at that, with blue-black swirling currents.

"It looks like we'd better pick up the pace!" said Kate.

Ben and Kate ran downstairs and helped Mum move everything else out of the living room, packing vases and pictures in bubble wrap and heaving the rug up the stairs. When they'd finished, they looked around at the empty room. The floorboards were bare and dusty, and there were pale patches on the wall where the pictures had been.

"It looks so much bigger with nothing in it," said Ben. "We should have it like this all the time. I could set up my Scalextric in here."

"You'll be lucky!" Mum said, laughing.

"Shh – wait," said Kate. "Can anyone hear that whining?"

It seemed to be coming from the kitchen. They trooped down the hall and found Jess lying under the kitchen table. She looked up at them with big, sad eyes.

"Poor thing. She hates thunderstorms," said Kate.

"Don't worry, Jess," said Ben, crouching down to scratch her head. He crawled under the table, and Jess laid her head on his lap and wagged her tail. "That's better," said Ben, tickling her under the chin.

He stayed under the table with Jess while Kate helped Mum to check they had enough food in the cupboards in case they were flooded in.

"We've got lots of tins – that should

keep us going for a few days, at least,"
said Mum.

"Amazing. Do we get to have baked
beans for dinner every night?" asked Kate.

"Yessss! And spaghetti hoops!" said Ben.

"And mushy peas," said Mum, taking a
murky green tin out of the cupboard. She
looked at the back and grimaced. "Or
maybe not – I think this tin's older than
both of you."

Just then, Jess's ears pricked up. She raced from the kitchen down the hall and started barking. Ben stood up and went to follow her.

Jess was pawing at the back door, but when she saw Ben she raced up to him, panting. He bent down and ruffled her fur.

"Is the thunder bothering you, girl?" he asked.

Jess's favourite toy, a squishy red bone, lay on the floor. Ben picked it up and held it out to her. "Here, Jess. . ." he said, crouching down. She padded up to him and settled down to gnaw the bone, her tail beating out a rhythm on the carpet.

Ben felt vibrations from the thunder beneath his feet. He looked out through the back door – the world outside was flashing between bright white and moody grey, as if someone in the sky was flicking a light switch on and off, over and over again.

He peered through the blurry glass. Everything looked very different than it had this morning. Big puddles, almost the size of ponds, were forming on the lawn. The daffodils were being buffeted this way and that by the wind, and he could hear the rain pummelling the fence at the bottom of the garden. He looked past the fence to the field beyond and gasped – he couldn't see it. It seemed to have disappeared.

Ben could still see the little hill at the end of the field, and there was the oak tree standing on top, its leaves dancing in the wind . . . but all around the hill, instead of grass, there was dark, muddy water. *We really are so lucky our house is on high ground*, he thought. The flooded part of the field was only a football-pitch's length away. He crossed his fingers, hoping and hoping that the water wouldn't rise any higher.

And that was when he saw them – Mr Green's sheep. They were crowded together on the hill, the only patch of dry land, looking around as though they were desperate for somewhere to escape to. Ben could see a few lambs, huddling close to their mothers for warmth, even more shaky than usual on their spindly legs. If the water got much higher, the hill would disappear under water, too – and then the sheep would have nowhere to go. *We have to get them to safety*, he thought. *But how?*

3

"Mum! Kate! The field – the sheep –
underwater. . ." Ben burst through the
kitchen door, breathless, with Jess running
ahead of him.

"Slow down," said Mum as Ben struggled to get his words out. "Start again. What's going on?"

"The bottom field has flooded! And Mr Green's sheep are still out there!"

"What? No way – he should have moved them by now," said Kate.

"Come and look!" said Ben, running back down the hall with Kate and Mum following close behind. Ben stood aside so they could peer through the steamed-up glass of the back door to see for themselves.

Kate shook her head. "Those sheep – and those lambs! They're so tiny! We've got to call Mr Green!"

"Do you have his number, Mum?" said Ben.

"Yes, it's on the fridge. . ."

Ben dashed back to the kitchen and

scanned the front of the fridge. It was covered in bills, receipts and family photos, held up by embarrassing magnets from holidays they'd been on years ago – but he couldn't see Mr Green's number anywhere.

Just as he was losing hope, he lifted up a bank statement to see if anything was underneath it. And there it was – a scrap of paper with "Mr Green" scrawled on it, peeping out from under a pineapple-shaped magnet. He snatched it up and ran back to give it to Mum.

"Brilliant, Ben," said Mum. She picked up the phone and dialled quickly. Ben and Kate watched her anxiously, waiting for Mr Green to pick up. But Mum just frowned and looked at the receiver.

"There's no dial tone," she said. "The phone lines must be down."

She grabbed her mobile from the kitchen table and dialled the number again. Ben held his breath.

"No reception!" she cried.

"Don't worry, Mum – let me try," said Kate, taking her mobile out of her pocket. "I always get reception at the bottom of the garden."

Kate grabbed the scrap of paper, pulled her soaking wet raincoat and wellies on again, and ran to the back door. Jess scampered after her, barking, thrilled at having another opportunity to chase someone.

"Hold Jess! Don't let her come after me," called Kate as she banged the back door shut and walked out into the garden, hunching against the rain.

Ben watched through the kitchen window as Kate stood by the garden fence and dialled Mr Green's number. She was getting wetter by the second. "Still ringing," she mouthed.

"Why isn't he picking up?" asked Ben. But then Kate made a thumbs-up sign, and started chatting animatedly on the phone.

"At last!" said Mum, squeezing Ben's shoulder. Ben gave a sigh of relief – but when he looked back at Kate, she seemed worried again.

"Now what?" asked Ben as Kate ran back to the house.

"It's no good – he can't come," said Kate. "He's stuck at the farm – a tree has fallen down and there's no way he can get across the road. We're going to have to think of some other way to get those sheep out of there."

No one said anything for a minute.

"Do you think *we* could get them out?" asked Ben. "I've watched Mr Green herd his sheep. . ."

"But we aren't trained herders," said Mum. "It would be dangerous to try moving them when we don't know what we're doing – we might end up scaring them into even deeper water."

They were silent again. *This is so silly*, thought Ben. *If I was stuck at the bottom of the field and couldn't get out, Mum would call an ambulance, or maybe the fire brigade. There should be something like that for animals.*

And then he realized there was. "Why don't we call the RSPCA?" said Ben.

"Of course! Yes!" said Kate. "Brilliant idea. Why didn't I think of that?"

"Because I'm cleverer than you," said Ben, making a face. Kate made one back – but then she gave him a sloppy kiss on the cheek. Ben wiped it off with his sleeve.

Mum nodded. "That's a great idea, Ben," she said. "Let's give them a call. I think they have a twenty-four-hour number for emergencies. Let's hope they're not too tied up with all the other flooding in the area."

Kate jumped up. "The internet's working on my phone – I'll get the number. Keep your fingers crossed!"

She loaded the RSPCA website on her phone and ran back to the bottom of the garden to dial the number. Ben pulled on his wellies and raincoat and followed Kate. As she waited for the RSPCA to answer, he stood on tiptoes and peered over the garden fence at the sheep in the field below. The hill where the sheep were standing was almost

covered in water now. Ben felt helpless —
he was so close to them, but there was
nothing he could do. "Please let the
RSPCA get here soon," Ben whispered
to himself.

"Hello? Yes! Yes, I want to report an
emergency . . . there are sheep stranded
in a flooded field at the bottom of our
garden. . . Yes, Hazelbrook Farm, near
Tipperton. . ." Ben listened to his sister

giving the RSPCA detailed instructions.

"How many sheep can you see in the field?" she asked Ben. Ben counted them, glad he could do something to help. "Thirty? Thirty-five, maybe?" he said. "Not sure exactly how many, though . . . they keep moving around."

Kate passed on the information. As she hung up the phone, she punched Ben gently on the arm. "Don't worry – they'll be here in no time."

Ben nodded and forced a smile. He just hoped Kate was right.

Ben and Kate squelched their way back through the muddy grass to the back door, where Mum and Jess were waiting for them.

"What time will they be here?" Mum asked as Kate and Ben filed past her into the hall.

"In about half an hour, hopefully," said Kate.

"Right. There's nothing we can do for the moment, then," said Mum. "Why don't we have something to eat? It's nearly teatime, and we'll need lots of energy for when the RSPCA get here."

"What about a picnic?" suggested Kate.

"Good plan," said Mum. "We have bread and cheese, and there's cupcakes and biscuits for anyone who's really hungry."

Ben fetched the picnic blanket from upstairs and spread it on the living room floor while Kate unpacked plates and cups from one of the cardboard boxes. She laid them on the blanket, and Mum served up a feast of cheese, bread and cakes.

Ben had just finished his final mouthful of cupcake when the doorbell rang.

"It must be them!" he said, putting down his plate and rushing down the hall. His heart pounded as he opened the door to find a man and a woman standing on the doorstep. They were dressed in the same uniform — navy blue trousers, black wellington boots, and navy waterproof jackets — but otherwise they couldn't have looked less alike.

The woman was the same height as Kate, with friendly blue eyes and blonde curly hair that looked like it was trying to escape from her head. The man had short black hair and dark brown eyes, and he was the tallest person Ben had ever seen in his life.

The woman smiled and reached out her hand to shake Ben's, and he squeezed it tightly.

"That's a firm handshake!" she said, wincing slightly.

"Thanks! I'm Ben," he said.

"I'm Annie, and this is Dan," she said, as the man stepped forward to shake Ben's hand, too.

"Thanks so much for coming," said Ben, formally, holding the door open for them. Everything felt very official now that they'd shaken hands.

"The sheep are in the field at the bottom of our garden," said Ben. "There are lambs out there, too. You'll be able to get them on to dry land, right?"

"We're going to do our best," said Dan with a smile, "but we'll have to see how high the water level is. It's possible we'll have to call for a specialist flood team if it's too deep." Ben nodded and followed Dan down the hall.

Mum and Kate came out to meet them. "The garden's this way," said Mum, leading them to the back door.

They walked across the grass to the fence at the bottom of the garden and looked out over the field below.

"There are quite a few lambs, aren't there?" said Annie.

"Yes, I counted seven," said Kate.

"They were only born a couple of

weeks ago," said Mum. "The world isn't making them feel very welcome so far."

Had the lambs only been born two weeks ago? Ben thought to himself. It felt like years had passed since then. He had grown so fond of them – he loved going down to the bottom of the garden before school to watch them leaping about in the morning light, chasing each other and their own tails until they tumbled on to the grass in a heap. They looked as though they were too cold and wet to chase each other now. . .

"Right," said Dan, "let's get this show on the road. It looks like all the low-lying fields are flooded. But this one is so high above water level, there's almost no risk of it flooding," he said, pointing to a field to the right of the garden, right next to Mr Green's farmhouse.

"But how are you going to get the sheep in there?" asked Kate, leaning on the fence. "There's no gate from the bottom field into that one."

"Oh, but there is," Dan said, rubbing his hands together. "There's one right here." He patted their garden gate. "Could we lead the sheep through your garden?"

"Of course," said Mum.

"Great," smiled Dan. "Then we can herd them out through the gate up there – that leads into the field, right?"

He pointed to a wooden gate in the fence on the right of the garden, near the house, which led to the next-door field. Ben had almost forgotten it existed – it stood between the trellises of roses and jasmine and was barely visible beneath a tangle of thorns and pale-pink rosebuds. Ben couldn't remember ever walking through it – when they were little, Kate had told him it was a gateway into a different world.

"I knew Dad must have built that gate for a reason!" said Mum. "We never use it – it's probably a bit rusty."

"That doesn't matter, as long as it opens!" said Annie. Ben ran over to test it. He pushed down on the metal catch. It was stiff, but it soon sprang upward. He leaned on the gate and it swung open with a high-pitched squeak.

"Brilliant," said Dan. "Plan A is on. Let's talk tactics. We'll form a line behind the sheep—"

"Wait – don't you need more than two people to herd sheep?" said Ben.

"Definitely," said Dan, "but we have more than two."

Ben was confused. "Are you waiting for more RSPCA officers to arrive?" he asked.

"No – we were hoping the three of you might give us a hand," said Dan.

"Us? Really? We can help?" said Ben.

"We can't do it without you," said Annie.

"Are you up for it?" asked Dan.

"Yes," said Ben and Kate.

"Absolutely," said Mum.

"Great!" said Annie. "Here's what we have to do. . ."

Annie and Dan gave everyone a quick sheep-herding training session. "We need to join hands in a line behind the sheep and encourage them to walk through the water, up the slope and into the garden. The water is still quite shallow – ankle-deep at most. None of you will be in any danger," said Annie.

"Just make sure you don't let go of each other's hands," said Dan as they formed a line and practised creeping slowly and quietly through the garden.

"Perfect," said Annie.

"Is Jess coming with us?" said Ben, as the line broke apart.

"I nearly forgot about her – thank goodness you reminded me!" said Mum.

"We'll have to keep her upstairs for a while. You know what she's like around sheep – she gets too excited. She's a hopeless sheepdog – that's why she retired!"

She marched off towards the house, and Ben heard Jess yapping as Mum led her upstairs. He was a bit disappointed – he'd been looking forward to whistling signals to Jess, the way he'd seen farmers do in sheepdog trials on the TV. But when he heard Dan, Annie and Kate discussing what to do when they got the sheep into the garden, he felt too excited and nervous to think about anything but the rescue.

"Let's get started," said Dan as Mum hurried back through the garden.

"Just remember," said Dan, move quickly but quietly, and don't let go of each other's hands."

Everyone nodded. Ben looked at his watch – it was just after four. Usually at this time he'd have just arrived home from school, but today he was about to take part in an animal rescue. His heart began to race – this was really happening.

4

"Great work, everyone," called Annie. "We're halfway there now. . ."

Ben looked up from the ankle-deep water and glanced at his watch – it had taken them about five minutes to walk down the slope to the middle of the field, but it felt like they'd been walking for hours. He'd forgotten how much hard work walking through water was – he felt like he was lifting a huge weight every time he took a step. He wanted to move faster, but knew he might end up falling over, like he did every time he raced his friends to see who could run furthest into the sea. *I really don't fancy swallowing a mouthful of this murky green water*, he thought, looking at it swirling around his wellies.

Dan motioned for everyone to stop walking. They were at the flattest part of the field now – the little hill where the sheep were sheltering under the oak tree was only about ten paces away. The rain was lighter than it had been, but it was still pitter-pattering on the water's surface, and gathering in droplets on the sheep's wool.

"Right, we don't want the sheep to notice us," said Annie in a low voice. "Let's split up into two lines – I'll head to the right, and Dan will head left. Ben and Kate, you come with me. . ."

"Which leaves you with me," said Dan, smiling at Mum.

"We're going to circle around the back of the sheep, and meet up when we're on the other side of the hill. That way they won't know they're being surrounded," said Annie.

"Like a pincer movement," said Ben.

"Exactly!" said Dan, grinning. "OK, let's get going. Remember to keep your voices down – we don't want the sheep to hear us," he said. They all crouched down and circled around behind the hill. Ben moved his feet as slowly as he could, so that they wouldn't make any noise.

They managed to get behind the sheep without spooking them, and soon they were standing at arm's length from one another in a semicircle.

"When I say so, we'll join hands in a line and walk over the hill," whispered Dan. "One . . . two. . ."

Ben tried to take a step towards Kate with his left foot and realized he couldn't move it. His boot was well and truly stuck in the mud.

He tried to yank his leg out with his hands but nothing happened. Then he tried to grab hold of the boot and pull that out, but it was no good. Kate came over to help.

"Hold on to my back to keep steady," she said, bending over and grabbing hold of his leg.

"Ready? One . . . two. . ." *SLURP!* Ben staggered backwards, free at last – but their cover was blown. The sheep started running this way and that, changing directions at the last minute, butting into one another in their rush to escape.

"OK, next stage of the operation," said Dan, not bothering to be quiet any more. "It's time to join hands – don't let them past you!"

Ben reached out his left hand to Kate, who grabbed it. Annie caught his right hand. "Let's keep them moving towards your garden," she called, raising her voice so she'd be heard over the sheep who were now baaing loudly.

The sheep were big close-up – they

came up to Ben's waist – but the lambs were even tinier than he remembered. He wished he could scoop them all up and tuck them somewhere cosy with a hot-water bottle, or at least reach down to pat them and reassure them, but he knew that first he needed to get them out of the water as quickly as possible. So he held tight to Annie and Kate's hands and tried to keep the sheep moving up the slope towards the garden. Some of the animals stumbled and fell to their knees as they tried to find footholds in the slippery mud, but they soon got up again.

It was like a really difficult computer game, trying to guess which way to dodge to stop the sheep slipping through the gaps in their arms. At first Ben felt nervous – he didn't want to hurt or upset the sheep. He soon felt more confident, and tried to shoo the sheep towards the garden – but although they headed that way at first, they either stopped stubbornly a metre away from the herders or sped off to the right or left, forcing Dan and Annie to dive and stop them.

"Something tells me they really don't want to leave this field," said Kate, trying to stop a determined-looking ewe from running in the wrong direction.

"I don't blame them. I wouldn't want to walk through all that water, either," said Ben.

But gradually the sheep grew calmer. Annie had noticed that the sheep all seemed to be following one ewe in particular, so she concentrated on herding her towards the garden. As soon as she started trotting up the slope, the others followed.

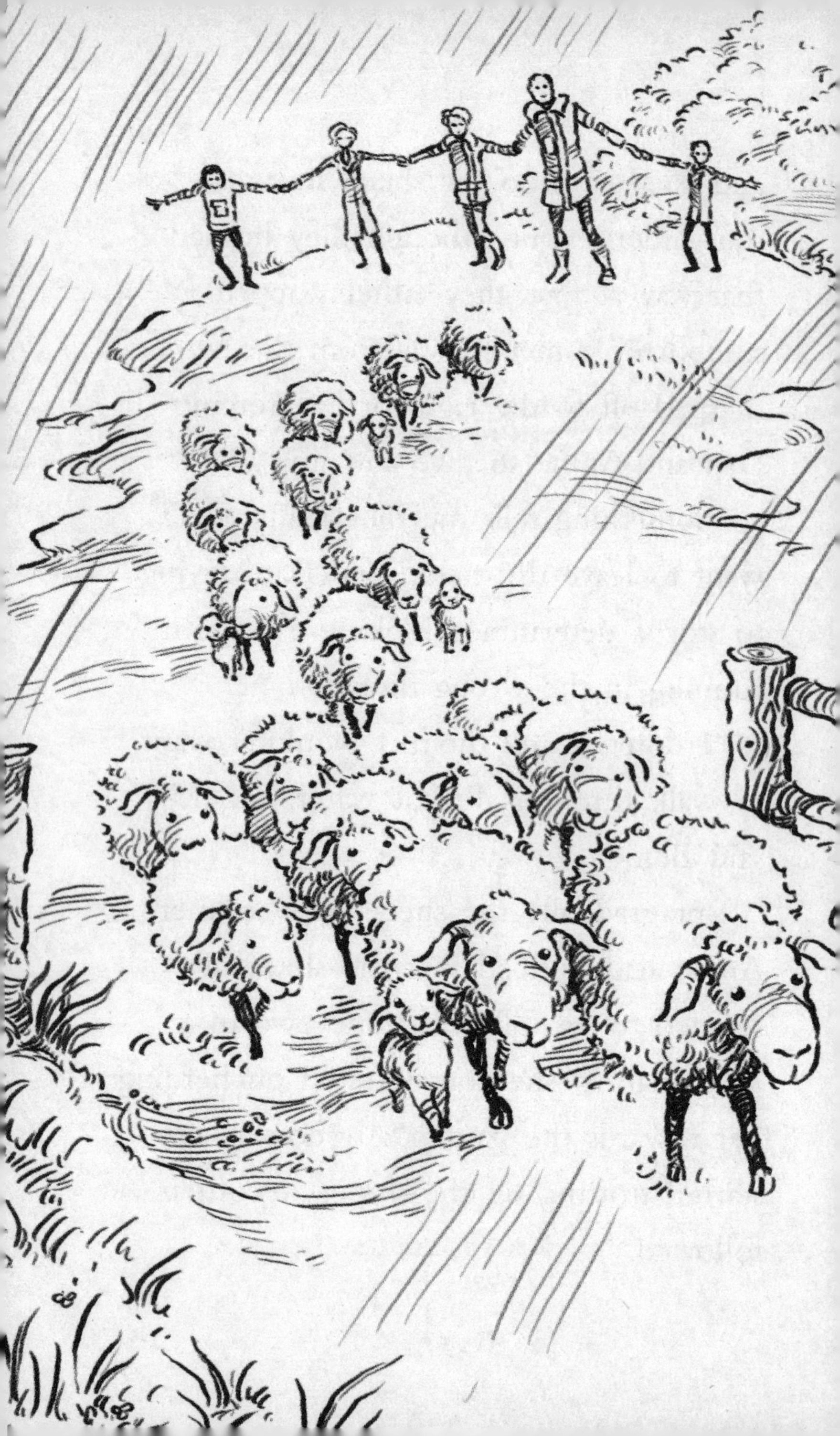

"Right, I think we're getting somewhere," said Dan.

Ben looked up. Through the streaming rain it looked as though a white river of sheep was flowing up the slope – but he could see that one ewe kept trying to dart out to the side. Dan kept nudging her back into the circle and coaxing her forward.

"Come on, girl," he said, "there's loads of lovely fresh grass up there – why would you want to swim around down here in the mud?" The sheep didn't look convinced, but she started reluctantly moving forward with the rest of the flock, looking back over her shoulder at the field below.

They were nearly at the garden gate now. Mum left her place in the line and rushed ahead to open it. She held it open for the sheep to walk through, but instead they came to a shuddering halt and started to stumble backwards into each other.

"They can probably smell Jess," said Kate.

"Or see her!" said Ben, pointing to his parents' bedroom window. Kate glanced up to look. Jess was pawing forlornly at the glass. There was such a look of hurt in her eyes, as if she were saying, *You KNOW how much I love herding sheep. And now you're bringing thirty-five of them through my back garden? And I'm not allowed to chase even one? Not even a little one?*

"Are you sure we can't let her help, Mum?" said Ben. "I've been training her up. . ."

"Yes, to herd your friends! I don't

think that's quite the same as herding sheep," said Mum.

"Spoilsport," grumbled Ben.

"Wait – I have an idea," said Mum. She reached down, pulled up a clump of grass and held it out to the ewe that seemed to be leading the flock.

The ewe sniffed the grass and bent down to take a bite, but Mum moved the grass out of her reach. She walked backwards, holding out the grass, and the sheep followed her right through the gate. Once one sheep had walked into the garden, the others followed, and soon they were all trotting on to the lawn.

"You've done this before!" said Annie, beaming, as the sheep streamed past her.

Mum shrugged. "I grew up on a farm," she said. Ben and Kate looked at each other and raised their eyebrows. They were impressed.

Dan made sure the last of the sheep were safely in the garden and swung the gate closed behind him.

"Brilliant effort, everyone," said Annie as they all tried to catch their breath.

"Right," said Dan, "now all we have to do is get the sheep out of the garden and into the field. Piece of cake."

Ben looked around the garden at the sheep, which were munching on the lawn and nibbling at the primroses. They seemed much happier now – the lambs were snuggled up under their mothers.

"OK, get ready to play Little Bo Peep again," said Annie, as they joined hands once more.

"Wait, didn't she lose her sheep?" said Ben.

"Yes," said Kate, "and she wore a silly bonnet. We're way cooler than her."

"Yeah, we'll be cowboys instead," said Ben.

"Whatever we are, it's time to get moving," said Annie. "Let's get these sheep off your lawn and into that dry field!"

They all joined hands again and formed a line. They started walking slowly towards the gate, trying to keep the sheep moving forward and stop them nibbling the flowers. Some of the sheep kept getting distracted by tasty patches of grass, but most of them seemed happy to follow the rest of their flock. Ben loved watching the way the sheep looked after their lambs – they called out for their babies whenever they lost sight of them, and the lambs skipped eagerly up to their mothers when they heard them bleating.

Soon the last of the sheep were trotting through the gate. There was just one ewe left, with her tiny lamb. Up close, it was more grey than white, and a little wrinkly still – it looked as though it was wearing a fleecy blanket. It tripped as it was walking through the gate and gave a high-pitched little *Baa!* but its mother nudged it forward.

Soon they, too, were safely in the field.

"We did it!" called Ben, swinging the gate shut. He looked at the sheep in the dry field – they looked relaxed and happy now. The lambs were hopping around, tripping over their legs, and most of the sheep were starting to eat the grass. But one of the ewes still didn't look happy. She stood at the far end of the field, looking down at the flood below, bleating and bleating as though she was calling out for something – but what?

Ben looked down at the flooded field, too. The muddy water looked like it would be deep enough to swim in now – he couldn't believe it had been full of grazing sheep this morning. The drystone wall that marked the edge of the field was only just visible now above the flood, and only a tiny patch of the hill was still above the flood level – it looked as though it were trying to keep its head above water. The oak tree was still standing proudly on top of the hill, although it did have a few broken branches. Ben's eyes travelled down the trunk of the tree – and that's when something caught his attention: a tiny flash of white, there and then not there, as though someone was standing behind the tree, waving a handkerchief. Ben felt dread building up inside him as he realized what it must be. How could they have missed it? And what were they going to do now?

5

"Annie," he said, grabbing her arm, "can you see that? Behind the oak tree?"

"No. . ." said Annie, squinting in the direction he was pointing. "What is it?"

"Something white – I saw it just now. There it is again!"

"I think it's just a bit of wool caught on a branch," said Annie slowly.

"No, it isn't," said Dan, as a tiny head with pink folded ears appeared from behind the tree. It was a lamb – they'd left a lamb behind!

Ben held his breath as it tottered out

from behind the tree and started looking around. It was as though it had only just realized it was all alone.

"Poor thing," said Mum. "It's absolutely tiny."

The lamb was bleating and bleating – and to their right they heard a sheep baaing back. They seemed to be calling to each other.

"It's that ewe, the one who didn't want to leave the field — she must be the mother," said Annie.

"Well, let's get the lamb out of there, then," said Kate. But no one moved.

"It's not as simple as that any more," said Dan. "We need to see how high the water level is — if it's too deep, we won't be able to just carry the lamb to safety in our arms."

"And what if it *is* too deep?" Ben asked anxiously.

"Let's cross that bridge when we come to it," said Dan.

Ben and Kate looked at each other, shocked. The rescue had been exciting up until now — even though Ben knew the sheep had been in danger, he'd never doubted that the RSPCA would get them out safely, and Annie and Dan had been so relaxed and confident. But they didn't look so relaxed now. Annie had a deadly serious expression on her face as she dialled a number on her mobile phone and walked to the other end of the garden. Dan looked equally grim as he unclipped the black radio from his belt. He held it to his ear, and it crackled just like a police radio.

"Hi, it's Dan here. We're at Hazelbrook Farm between Tipperton and Brownmere – are there any flood rescue teams in the area? Over."

"Give me a second while I check if any of the teams are free. Over," said a muffled voice at the other end. Usually Ben would have been seriously excited to hear people in real life saying "over" as if they were spies or soldiers, but right now he was too worried about the lamb to care about anything else.

A few moments later, the voice said, "Dan? Afraid everyone is completely tied up – we can't send anyone out to you right now. Will you be OK on your own? Over."

"We'll have to be – thanks anyway," said Dan, sighing. "Over and out."

"Any luck?" said Annie, walking back to them.

"No," said Dan. "All the flood teams are out already. You? Did you try the fire service?"

"Yes – they're busy with other emergencies."

"Well, I'll go down and check the water level anyway," said Dan. "I have to get my flood gear on first, though . . . it's in the van."

"I'll come with you – I'll need to let

you back through the front door," said
Mum.

The others waited in tense silence
until Mum and Dan came back. Dan
looked like a cross between an astronaut

and Fireman Sam in his flood gear –
waterproof trousers, wellies, a bright
yellow jacket and helmet, and a red life
jacket. He opened the garden gate and
headed straight for the field, running
down the slope until he reached the
water. Then he started walking into the
flooded field – quickly at first, then more
and more slowly as the water got deeper.

Ben leaned on the garden fence and
looked past Dan to the hill where the
tiny lamb was standing in front of the
tree, bleating. It looked so cold and
lonely.

"Will it be OK, Mum?" asked Ben.

"I hope so, darling," said Mum, putting
her arm around him. Ben didn't usually
let Mum hug him any more – and he
hated it when she called him darling –
but he didn't mind this time.

Ben could see Dan was up to his waist
in water now, and he was still wading
through the field. The water crept slowly
up Dan's body with every step he took,
and when he reached the middle of the
field, still quite a way from the lamb, he
turned round. He was up to his armpits
in water.

Annie nodded. "Chest height for Dan –

and he's nearly two metres tall. It'll be almost shoulder height for the rest of us! This is going to be tricky."

Dan started walking back up the slope towards them.

"But can you still rescue the lamb?" asked Ben.

"Well, the water's far too high for Dan to pick it up and carry it back to dry land – it's too risky. He'd have to hold the lamb above his head to keep it out of the water, and the poor thing won't know we're trying to save it, so it'll try to get away. If he slips, they could both be in danger. We're going to have to think of another way to get it to safety."

"Don't you have life rafts? I'm sure I saw you using something like that on the news once," said Kate.

Annie shook her head. "The flood

teams have them – they're all being used."

"But there'll be more at your headquarters, right?" said Kate.

"Yes, but the centre's almost an hour's drive away. By the time someone brings us one it'll be too late," said Annie.

"Too late?" Ben felt sick.

Annie looked out at the field. "I hope not. We'll do our best – but if we don't manage to reach the lamb before dusk, we'll have to abandon the rescue. It's not safe to go out in a flood when it's dark."

Ben could hear his heart beating in his ears. "And what would happen to the lamb if you abandoned the rescue?"

"Well, we'd have to come back in the morning."

"But if it doesn't stop raining, the water will get even deeper. . ."

"Hopefully it won't come to that," said

Annie. She looked at her watch – it was half past five. "We have about an hour and a half to get the lamb to dry land."

"OK, people – we need to think of a plan, and quick," said Kate. But no one seemed to have any ideas. Ben swallowed. He couldn't believe it. Surely there must be *something* they could do?

6

"Listen," said Kate, her hands on her hips.
"I'm a lifeguard – what if I swim out
there and rescue the lamb myself? I don't
need a life raft to rescue people, and a
lamb is much smaller than a human. I
think I could do it."

"It's just too dangerous," said Annie.
"Humans usually cooperate when you're
trying to save their lives, but lambs
don't – and, believe me, one of the first
things a lamb learns is how to kick."

"I've been kicked by kids before. . ."
said Kate.

"But children don't have hooves," Annie pointed out. "Rescuing animals is really quite a different skill. You can't do it without something to put the lamb on — something that floats. I'm sorry, we can't risk you coming to any danger."

Kate frowned and folded her arms. She hated being told no. Then her face brightened again.

"What about the sports shop in town? They sell foam floats — that might work? Dad should be coming home soon. Maybe he could pick one up on his way."

"Already thought of that," said Annie. "They're closed, because of the flood."

Kate let out a frustrated sigh. Ben could tell she was really annoyed that she wasn't being allowed to help — and he was, too, because he was sure she'd be able to save the lamb. He'd never admit it – she'd be far too smug about it – but she was a brilliant lifeguard.

He'd seen her practising lifesaving with her friends at the beach. When her friend John had pretended to get into difficulties, she hadn't hesitated for a second – she'd grabbed her surfboard and paddled over to him in lightning-quick time. Ben had watched, amazed, as she hauled him on to the surfboard in front of her and steered them both safely back to the shore.

Suddenly, Ben had an idea. "Just a minute," he said.

Ben ran back to the house as fast as he could, crashing through the back door, ignoring his mum's shouts of "Where are you going?" He leaped up the stairs two at a time and reached Kate's bedroom door slightly breathless. Plastered across the door were "Keep out!" signs. Kate had scribbled "Especially younger brothers" on a piece of paper and stuck that underneath, too, but Ben knew he'd be forgiven for ignoring it this one time. He burst into the room and looked around.

He hadn't been in Kate's room for a while – he'd forgotten how untidy she was. The walls were invisible beneath posters of surfers and bands. He could hardly see the floor either – it was strewn with dirty clothes, cereal bowls and magazines. It was even messier than *his* room.

Ben hopped between piles of T-shirts and eventually reached Kate's wardrobe. He opened it up, and saw it at once –

Kate's surfboard. It was jammed at the back, behind a tangle of sports equipment and clothes she never wore any more. Ben pushed some coats and a hockey stick out of the way and grabbed the edges of the board. He pulled and pulled, but he couldn't get it out – it

was wedged tightly against the sides of the cupboard.

Ben glanced out of Kate's bedroom window – it was getting darker. He had no time to lose. He gripped the surfboard again, squeezing his eyes tight with the effort, and leaned backwards, pulling at it as hard as he could. Just as it shifted a little bit, he heard Kate's voice floating up from the garden.

"I'm just going to see where Ben's got to. . ." He heard her running through the back door and bounding up the stairs.

"What's going on?" she asked, poking her head around the door.

"I had an idea – your surfboard! Why don't we try to get the lamb out of the field on that?"

"Good thinking!" she said. "But let me

get it out of the cupboard. I'm much stronger than you."

"As if!" said Ben. He stepped out of the way and Kate squeezed herself into the wardrobe and began tugging at the surfboard. Ben had to admit she seemed to be doing a better job than him. Maybe she was a little bit stronger after all, but even she was having trouble. "I must – keep – this – somewhere – else – in the – oof! Future!" she said, tumbling backwards on to Ben and pulling the surfboard with her.

"You nearly squashed me to death!" Ben cried, moving out from underneath his sister.

"Got the surfboard out, though, didn't I?" said Kate. "Nice teamwork." She gave him a high five and helped him up from the floor.

"Let's take an end of the board each," said Kate. They bent down to pick it up and edged their way out of the room and down the stairs.

Annie, Dan and Mum were talking in hushed tones as Kate and Ben walked out into the garden. "What on earth have they got there?" said Mum as they all turned to look.

"Your children are geniuses," said Dan as they got closer.

"Ben thought we could use my surfboard — what do you reckon?" said Kate, setting it down.

"Inspired idea," said Annie. "This is exactly what we need. Nice one, Ben."

Dan turned to Annie, and they spoke to each other quietly for a moment. Then Dan turned back to the others. "Right — I'm going to lead the rescue and go down into the field. Annie's going to coordinate everything from here — she's got a radio, so she can call for backup if we need it."

"But don't you need two people to carry out the rescue?" asked Kate.

"Well, you're the expert surfer, aren't you?" asked Dan. "And you're used to rescuing people on surfboards, right? I was hoping you'd come with me. What do you say?"

Everyone looked at Kate. "Yes, definitely!" she said, her eyes shining.

"Great!" said Annie. "You'll need something to wear . . . do you have a wetsuit?"

"Let me go and grab it," said Kate, and she ran back into the house.

Ben was relieved they finally had a plan to rescue the lamb, but a tiny part of him was disappointed. He really wished he could do something to help, too. He looked at the ground, making a trail in the mud with his wellies.

"Are you OK, Ben?" asked Annie.

"Yes," he said, looking up.

"Wish you were going with Dan, too?" asked Annie. Ben nodded. "But there's loads you can do to help without going into the water," she went on. "That's why I'm staying out here – I'm on standby in case anything goes wrong, and to get everything ready for the lamb. You could help with that – we need someone to sort out some warm blankets and towels so we can get the lamb warm and dry as soon as possible."

"OK – shall I do that now?" asked Ben.

"That would be brilliant," said Annie, and Ben set off towards the house. As he walked through the back door Kate passed him, dressed in her wetsuit.

"I'm ready!" Ben heard her call to the others.

Ben shut the back door behind him and got to work straight away, hunting down every blanket in the house – he wanted to get outside again as soon as possible so he wouldn't miss a second of the rescue. He could hear Dan telling the others to hurry up. He looked at his watch – it was already ten to six. It would be getting dark in about an hour. There wasn't a moment to lose.

7

Ben gathered up the family's tartan picnic rug, the fleecy blanket on Kate's bed, and the cashmere throw that Mum

always wrapped herself in when they were watching TV. He collected a pile of towels – the fluffiest he could find – and put them on the heated towel rail in the bathroom for a moment, to make them extra cosy. Then he stuffed them all in a plastic bag, so they wouldn't get wet, and dashed out into the garden, leaving the bag by the back door for when they needed it.

As he ran over the slippery mud to the garden fence, he could hear Dan and Kate discussing their plan of action. "Are you sure she's going to be safe out there?" Mum asked Annie.

Kate overheard. "Mum, I'm a lifeguard," she said.

"But it's getting darker every minute. What if you get stuck out there?"

"I won't!"

"Really, she won't," said Dan, fiddling with his life jacket. He unzipped a pouch at the back and pulled out a long yellow rope. "This is a safety line," he said, holding it up. "Annie's going to hold the end of mine, so in the very unlikely event I get into difficulties, she'll be able to tow me to safety. And you'll be holding on to Kate's safety line. Sound good?"

Mum nodded slowly. "I think I'd rather Annie held on to Kate's, if that's OK. She'll be much better at pulling her to safety."

"All right, then, but I'm relying on you to pull me in if I get into trouble," said Dan, smiling.

Dan threw a helmet to Kate. "You'll need this, too."

Kate caught it and strapped it on. Annie wobbled it on her head to make sure it was secure.

"That's it," she said. "You're good to go!"

Mum stopped Kate on her way to the garden gate and gave her a tight hug. Kate raised her eyebrows at Ben behind Mum's back.

"I'm literally going to the end of the bottom field, Mum – you know that, right? Not to Africa or anything."

"You're right," Mum said, flashing Kate and Dan a tight smile.

"OK – everyone ready?" asked Dan. "Ben, you stay here and watch. You two, follow me." Annie and Mum nodded. Ben waved them goodbye and watched as Dan opened the garden gate and led the others down the slope to the flooded part of the field. They stopped just before they reached the water, still quite a way from the hill where the lamb was standing. Dan helped Kate unzip the pouch at the back

of her life jacket and uncoil the long
yellow safety line. Kate tossed the end of
her line to Annie, and Dan passed his to
Mum.

"Wind the line around your hand like
this," Annie said to Mum. "That way you
won't let go of it." Mum nodded and
copied her, gripping the rope so tightly
that her knuckles turned white.

Kate followed Dan further into the
flooded field, holding her surfboard
by her side. Soon they were thigh-deep

in the water. By the time it was up to their waists, Kate was floating the surfboard in front of her, like an arrow pointing the way to the lamb. At last they were about two car-lengths away from the hill – and the water was almost up to their armpits.

It took them ages just to get that far, thought Ben. He looked at his watch – it was nearly six fifteen. Forty-five minutes till it got dark. Ben swallowed.

Kate and Dan were almost at the hill now. Even from the garden Ben could see that the lamb was trembling – but it wasn't making a sound. He pulled his jacket tighter around himself – looking at the lamb made him feel colder.

Ben heard Mum say to Annie, "It doesn't look like the lamb is bleating . . . that must be a bad sign."

"It might be in shock," said Annie, keeping her eyes firmly on Kate and Dan. "But I'm sure it'll be OK as soon as it's back on dry land."

Dan and Kate were at the bottom of the hill now. The lamb looked like it wasn't sure whether to move towards them or try to run away – but it had so little room to move that it just ended up chasing its tail around in a circle once before its legs collapsed beneath it. Ben saw Kate gasp as the lamb crumpled to its knees. She reached out her arms to the lamb, but the lamb just sat where it was.

Ben could see that Dan was giving instructions to Kate, but couldn't hear what he was saying. Kate nodded, and she and Dan grabbed hold of a side of the surfboard each, holding it steady. They

pushed it closer to the hill. The lamb let
out a weak little bleat and pushed itself
back up on to its hooves. It tottered
towards Kate and Dan but then it slipped
on a patch of mud and fell to its knees
again.

"Come on, little lamb," whispered Ben,
willing it to stand up.

Dan waded slowly up the hill, being
careful not to alarm the lamb, and bent
down to scoop it up.

The lamb seemed to have found its
voice at last. Ben could hear it bleating
and bleating as it wriggled around in
Dan's arms. Its mother galloped to the
edge of her field and cried out to it
through the fence. Ben raced through the
gate into the other field to comfort her.

"It's OK – your baby will be safe
soon," he said, trying to distract the ewe

with the lushest clump of grass he could find, but she only had eyes for her lamb.

Ben looked down to the bottom field again. Dan was walking down the hill towards the surfboard, stroking the lamb's soggy wool. Kate held the surfboard still, while Dan gently tied the lamb to the top of the board with a rope.

"Clever," said Mum. "Now there's no chance of the lamb falling into the water."

"Well done, guys!" she called as Dan and Kate started making their way back towards them. But then she turned to Annie and said, "It's already getting dark. They'd better not take too long. . ."

Ben looked around. It was as if someone had painted a dark grey wash over everything. But on the plus side, the rain was now just a light drizzle – hopefully that meant the flood waters wouldn't get any higher. . .

Kate paddled in the water, turning
the surfboard around so it was pointing
towards the garden again. She and Dan
swam alongside the board in silence, with
the lamb bobbing along between them,
bleating to its mother. The lamb looked
like it was surfing – Ben would have
found it funny at any other time, but
everything felt very serious now.

When they were halfway through the field, they stopped swimming and started wading, and Mum and Annie began to pull in the safety lines. Ben let out a breath he hadn't known he'd been holding.

Kate and Dan were walking more easily – the water reached their waists, then their thighs, and soon the water was so shallow that they didn't need the surfboard any more. Dan untied the lamb and picked it up, hugging it to him as he jogged up to the garden. Kate, Mum and Annie followed close behind. Ben opened the gate and dashed up to the back door to fetch the softest, warmest towel to wrap around the lamb.

"Nice work, Ben," said Dan, holding his hand out for the towel. He rubbed the lamb so roughly with it that Ben was afraid its ears would fall off.

"Don't hurt it!" said Ben.

"Don't worry, this little lamb is tougher than it looks – but the sooner we get it warm and dry, the better."

"We did it," said Kate.

"Well done, everyone," said Annie. "That was a true team effort."

"And the lamb will be OK, won't it?" said Ben.

"Come and see for yourself," said Dan. Ben peered over Dan's shoulder at the tiny bundle in the blue towel. The lamb's nose had a slightly purple tinge, and the lamb was still bleating, but it had stopped shivering.

"The only thing this lamb needs now is her mother," said Dan.

"Her?" asked Kate.

"Yes – she's a girl!" said Dan. "We

95

should probably put her somewhere warm tonight, but right now I think the best thing to do is to put her in the field with the rest of the sheep so she can feed."

Ben nodded. He was still gazing at the lamb, captivated by her tiny face.

She seemed small and delicate, and so peaceful now. And then – *ATISHOO!* – the lamb sneezed. Ben jumped backwards in shock.

"I didn't even know lambs *could* sneeze!" he said, laughing. He turned to Dan. "Could I hold her for a minute?" he asked.

"Well, she's not a pet, so it's best she doesn't get used to being held – but you can take her back to her mother if you like?" said Dan.

"Yes, please!" said Ben. He held out his arms, and Dan carefully passed the lamb

to him. The lamb gave a little bleat and
looked up at him with her big hazel eyes.
Ben was surprised how light she was. Her
wool felt a little bit rough at first, but
when he pushed his fingers deeper into
her fleece, it was deliciously cosy
and warm.

Ben walked through the gate into the
other field, and slowly bent down to put
the lamb on the grass. She didn't seem

to know what to do at first – she fell to her knees and looked around. But soon she was on her feet, trying out a few experimental steps. She teetered to the left, then to the right, and then she made a gigantic LEAP!

That caught the attention of the other sheep. The lamb's mother gave an almighty *BAAAA!* and galloped over to her. She slowed down to a trot as she reached her baby and lowered her head down to greet her. The lamb's eyes seemed to light up as she saw her mother. She gave a joyful-sounding bleat and snuggled up to the ewe, which nuzzled her – Ben could swear she was smiling.

"I wish you were that happy to see me when you come home!" said Mum. Kate put her arm around her. "We always are, Mum. We just show it differently. We

don't bleat so much."

As the lamb huddled underneath her
mother and began to feed, Annie sighed
contentedly. "This is the best part of
my job – seeing baby animals and their
mothers reunited. Well, that and getting a
pet settled in the perfect new home. . ."
To Ben it sounded like the best job in
the world.

★

The lamb had finished feeding and was curled up on the grass next to her mother. "I wish we could keep her," said Ben. *She'd get on well with Jess*, he thought. He could just imagine them chasing each other up and down the hall, or snuggled up together in front of the fire . . . but that wouldn't be fair on her. She had to run around in fields and grow up to have lambs of her own. . .

"Hey, don't worry," said Kate, ruffling his hair. "She lives just at the end of the garden — once the field has dried out, you can go and say hi whenever you like!"

8

"Now we just need somewhere warm for the lamb and ewe to stay for the night," said Dan. He turned to Mum. "Do you have a barn they could sleep in?" he asked.

"No . . . but there's a roof covering part of the field over there," she said, pointing to a sloping roof jutting out from one of Mr Green's farm buildings. Hay bales were piled high under the roof, but it was open to the elements on all sides.

"I don't think that would provide them with enough shelter," said Dan.

"What about our garage?" suggested Kate.

"Yes!" said Ben. "We never keep the car in there – it's just full of old junk."

"That sounds perfect," said Annie.

"We can clear out a corner and fill it with hay and straw. . ." said Kate.

"Sounds like a job for you two," said Mum. "Here are the keys." She tossed them to Ben.

"I'll give you a hand," said Dan. They walked back into the garden, and Dan shut the gate behind them. As they headed up the path by the side of the house, Ben looked over his shoulder – the ewe and the lamb were curled up together on the grass now, fast asleep.

They crunched across the gravel to the garage, and Ben pressed the button on the garage key. The door made a satisfying *zoom* noise as it rose slowly upward, revealing the mess within. Amid the rubbish, Ben could see the buggy Mum had pushed him to nursery in, their old kitchen table covered with cobwebs, and a box with "Ben's old toys" written on the side. He knew what was inside: his toy cars, some Lego and Sir Lancelot, the soft toy rabbit he'd taken everywhere until he was six (which he now pretended had never happened).

"Give me a hand, Ben!" Kate was already moving boxes and chairs to one side of the garage.

"We could get some hay bales from the field and block off a space for the lamb and her mother – that way they won't be able to jump out. Here, maybe?" she said, pointing to an area at the far left of the garage that was relatively free of spiders' webs.

"Great. You two clear that corner," said Dan. "I'll go and get some hay and straw."

Ben and Kate soon got into a rhythm: Kate picked up boxes and passed them to Ben, who tried to find somewhere to wedge them in the already packed garage.

Just as he was squeezing the final box between an old blow-up paddling pool and a mouldy-looking carpet, Dan came back, his head invisible behind a huge pile of straw.

"Oof!" he said, dropping it in the space they'd cleared. He kicked it about, spreading it out to make a soft bed for the sheep.

"Make way!" Annie and Mum edged into the garage, carrying two huge hay bales. They dropped them on the floor and pushed them together to form a wall around the straw bed.

"They'll be so cosy in there," said Annie.

"It looks way more inviting than my room," said Kate.

"That's because it doesn't have dirty clothes all over the floor!" said Ben. Kate nudged him playfully in the ribs.

"How will we get the lamb and her mother in here?" Mum asked Annie.

"That'll be easy, compared with the rescue," said Ben.

"Well, the ewe isn't just going to waltz in here, if that's what you think," said Annie. "But I do have a trick up my sleeve."

She led them to the side field. "Watch this," she said. She whispered to Dan, who nodded and picked up a handful of hay.

Then they tiptoed over to the lamb and her mother and while Dan was feeding hay to the ewe, Annie bent down and picked up the lamb. The lamb and the ewe baaed and baaed to each other.

"Don't worry," said Dan, stroking the ewe's head. "Your baby's right here."

Annie bent down and held the lamb

right in front of the ewe's nose. Then she
began to walk backwards, still holding the
lamb out in front of her.

"Ben, make sure I don't crash into
anything!" she called. Ben kept pace with
Annie as she walked backwards through
the field, shouting, "Left a bit — fence on
your right — you're coming to the end of
the field now. . ." The ewe followed Annie

and the lamb all the way through the field, up the path next to the house, and across the gravel to the garage.

"This is so cool!" said Ben.

"Coming through," called Annie as she backed into the garage. Ben and Kate rushed in front of her and pulled the hay bales apart so Annie could lead the sheep right into the straw-covered corner. The ewe followed Annie obediently, and as soon as she was standing on the straw, Annie gently put the lamb down next to her and slipped out. Kate and Ben pushed the hay bales back into place.

"We did it! Hooray!" said Ben.

"Could they be any more adorable?" asked Kate, looking down into the make-shift pen.

"Shall we give them names?" said Mum, looking at the lamb and her mother nestled together on the straw.

"What about 'Baaaaarbara' for the mum?" said Kate. Everyone groaned at the bad joke.

"The lamb can be called 'Lucky' – because she's really, really lucky we spotted her," said Ben.

"Now that's a good name," said Annie.

"What? Baaaaarbara is a good name, too," said Kate.

"If you say so," Annie said, laughing.

"Baaaaarbara and Lucky look totally at home," said Kate.

"Let's make them feel even more at home and get them some food and drink," said Dan.

"Yes – they'll need a bucket of water and some grass," said Annie.

"I'll get the water," said Kate.

"I'll gather some grass," said Dan.

"And I'll call Mr Green to tell him that his animals are safe and sound," said Mum.

"I think I'll stay here and watch Lucky and Baaaaarbara," said Ben. Baaaaarbara was lying contentedly on the straw, her legs tucked under her body. It looked like Lucky wanted to get her attention – she bleated and pawed her mum's back with her little hoof. Her mum didn't turn round, so Lucky bent her legs and sprang into the air, almost landing on Baaaaarbara's back. Ben laughed out loud for the first time since the rescue began – and once he started, he couldn't stop. But just then, he heard Kate say, "Look at that!" She was standing at the door of the garage with Annie, Dan and Mum.

"What is it?" asked Ben. He stood up and walked over to them. Kate pointed to

the sky, and Ben looked up. The rain had
stopped at last, and the clouds had cleared
to reveal an inky-blue sky, studded with
stars. Ben had never seen so many – they
lit up the night like a web of fairy lights.

"It's beautiful," said Mum.

"What a perfect end to the day," said

Kate. Ben nodded, breathing in the evening air. Now that the animals were safe, he didn't want the day to end.

9

"Can I tempt you both to stay for a cup
of tea and a hot cross bun?" Mum asked
Dan and Annie as they all walked back
towards the house. They looked at each
other. "We'll have to be getting back
soon," said Annie, "but a hot cross bun
wouldn't hurt – I could definitely do
with the energy after today!"

Once they were all crowded in the
kitchen, clutching mugs of tea and cocoa,
Ben realized how wet he really was. The
rain had got everywhere – even the inside

of his ears felt damp — and he began to shiver. He snuggled up against Jess, who was delighted to be downstairs again at last, and was sitting happily on his feet, wagging her tail.

Dan took a big gulp from his mug. "I think we'd better get back to the centre," he said. Annie nodded.

"But you can't go yet," said Ben, turning to the RSPCA officers. "What if it keeps raining and your van gets stuck? Then *you'll* need rescuing."

"I'm afraid we're going to have to take that risk," said Annie.

But before they could go anywhere, the doorbell rang.

"Maybe it's Dad," said Ben, rushing to the door.

"Why would it be him? He's got keys," said Kate, following Ben into the hall.

Ben opened the door to find a policeman standing on the doorstep.

"What is it, officer?" said Mum, rushing to the door. "Is everything OK?"

"Oh yes – nothing to worry about," the policeman assured. "I'm just doing the rounds to let you know that the flood warning has been lifted in this area."

"Thank you so much," said Mum, as though the policeman had stopped the flood himself.

"I propose a toast," said Dan, once they were all gathered in the kitchen again. He tapped his mug with his teaspoon, and everyone raised their mugs in the air.

"To Ben, Kate and Mum – animal rescuers extraordinaire."

"You can call me Sally," said Mum, laughing. Then she tapped her mug, too. "And to the RSPCA – I don't know

what we'd have done without you."

"To Lucky and Baaaaarbara!" said Annie.

"To all of us!" said Kate, and they all clinked their mugs together.

They drained the last of the cocoa from their cups – Ben stuck his tongue right to the bottom of his mug, so he could get to the delicious sticky undissolved cocoa powder. He ended up with a chocolatey moustache.

And then it really was time for Dan and Annie to leave. Everyone trooped outside to wave them off, and as Annie was getting into the van Ben tapped her on the shoulder.

"What's up, Ben?" said Annie.

"I just wanted to say thank you," Ben said. "I think what you do is so amazing."

"Thanks!" said Annie.

"I wish I could come back to the centre with you," added Ben.

"Well, you can't today, unless you're an injured lamb in disguise. . ." said Annie.

"*Baaaaa?*" he said, jokingly.

"Nice try!" said Dan, who was loading all of their kit into the van.

"But you can come and visit another day, if you like," said Annie.

"Really?"

"Sure," said Annie. "Ask your teacher to give us a call – your whole class could come and look around the centre. We can tell you more about the work we do, and show you some of the animals we look after."

"Yes, please!" said Ben.

Annie climbed up into the front of the van, next to Dan. "See you later!" shouted Dan, waving like crazy with

both hands as Annie started the engine. The engine gave a growl, and they drove off down the road, splashing through the puddles. Ben, Kate and Mum waved and waved until the van disappeared. As they walked back to the house, Ben realized he wasn't disappointed that their adventure was over after all – he was too excited about visiting the RSPCA centre, and introducing all of his friends to Dan and Annie.

"Don't you think it's time you had a bath, Ben? You need to dry off," said Mum as she shut the front door.

"Getting into a bath full of water won't get me dry." said Ben.

"Very clever." Mum smiled. "Decide between you and your sister who wants first bath – I'm going to run one now. . ."

"I'll come in a minute, Mum," said

Kate. "Let me just make some more cocoa first." Soon she and Ben were clutching refilled mugs of hot cocoa and talking about the day's events.

"It was so weird paddling through that field on my surfboard – we've been running around in it since we were, like, five, but I never thought I'd *swim* in it!"

"And can you imagine if I hadn't spotted Lucky? I wouldn't even have looked out of the window and seen the sheep if Jess hadn't started barking at the door!"

"Where *is* Jess?" said Kate, looking around the kitchen. Ben frowned – usually she'd be jumping all over him, trying to drink the cocoa out of his mug.

"Jess is having a bath," Mum called from the bathroom. "She didn't want the water to get cold – she's the only sensible one in this family." Ben and Kate looked at each other and pushed back their chairs at the same time. They loved bathing Jess – Mum hardly ever let her have a bath inside. They jostled each other as they ran upstairs to the bathroom and walked around the corner to see Mum sitting on the edge of the bath as Jess happily splashed around in the shallow water, frothing up the bubbles of the dog

shampoo as she wagged her tail. Ben reached into the bath and scooped up some bubbles. He piled them on Jess's head so it looked like she had a big white beehive hairdo.

"She looks like Gran!" said Kate, laughing, and then she plonked some bubbles on Ben's head in a Mohican shape.

"Please don't get your hair cut like that for real," said Mum, leaning down to scrub Jess. While Mum's back was turned, Ben and Kate exchanged glances.

"One," mouthed Kate. "Two," Ben continued, as they both quietly reached into the bath and skimmed off a handful of bubbles. . . "THREE!" said Kate, and they both planted their bubbles on Mum's head. Mum shrieked and flicked bubbles at Ben and Kate. They blinked and looked at

Mum in disbelief – she usually hated mess. "I can't believe you just did that!" said Ben.

"Well, it's not like anything could get wetter, could it?" Mum said with a shrug.

"That's it, it's war!" shouted Ben. But just as he was about to splash bubbles at Kate and Mum, the bathroom door crashed open.

"What on earth is going on here?" said a very confused voice.

"DAD!" chorused Ben and Kate. He was standing in the doorway, his hair still damp from the rain.

"Where have you been?" said Mum, standing up to hug him.

"I had to walk home. There was a tree blocking the road—"

"By Mr Green's farm?" asked Ben.

"Yes," said Dad, surprised. "How did you know? And – what on earth has happened to the house? There are an awful lot of muddy footprints in the hallway – and half a dozen mugs on the kitchen table. Have the army been here or something?"

"Almost. . ." said Mum. "Let's get clean and dry, and we'll tell you all about it."

Before long, Ben and Kate were in their pyjamas, sitting on the picnic blanket on the living room floor. Mum and Dad had ransacked the fridge and piled plates high

with salami, bread, tomatoes, cheese, jars of pickles and tins of anchovies, and they ate with their fingers. It felt like they were on a camping trip in the middle of nowhere.

"So, tell me all about your day," said Dad – but just then, the phone rang.

Mum stood up to answer it. "Hello, Mr Green," she said. Ben could just make out the farmer's deep voice on the other end of the line. "No need to thank us – we actually enjoyed rescuing the sheep! And the little lamb that's staying the night in our garage is the sweetest thing I've ever seen."

Dad froze, a piece of bread and cheese halfway to his mouth.

"Did she just say that there's a lamb in the garage?"

Kate and Ben looked at each other.

"Funny story. . ." said Kate.

★

"And now for the weather. It will be dry and sunny across the south of England. . ."

The sound of the radio drifted through the kitchen window to where Ben was standing at the bottom of the garden. He was leaning on the garden fence, his eyes closed, breathing in the delicious air. It smelled of flowers and grass and sunshine – maybe summer was finally on the way. . .

He opened his eyes and gazed down into the field below. It was hard to believe that it had been filled with murky brown water just three weeks ago – now it looked like a scene from an Easter card. The field was such a vivid shade of green it hardly looked real, and white clouds floated in the perfectly blue sky. Two of the clouds looked like sheep – one was big, and one was slightly smaller, just like

Baaaaarbara and Lucky.

"Lucky. . ." Ben called, looking around for his favourite lamb. He spotted her leaping around in the field with her friends. They bounced into the air as though they had springs in their legs — they seemed to be having a competition to see who could leap the highest.

Lucky had grown so much in the last few weeks. She was much less shaky on her legs now — and, just like the clouds in the sky, her wool had turned to a bright white.

"Here, Lucky!" Ben waved to attract her attention. She made one last leap into the air and came tumbling up to the fence. Ben bent down to stroke the curly wool on Lucky's head.

"Come inside, Ben!" called Mum. "It's almost time for school."

"Coming. . ." he replied. He pulled up a lump of lush green grass and held it out to Lucky. "I've got to go soon," he whispered, "but I'll be back tomorrow. And the next day . . . and the next!"

Meet A Real RSPCA Inspector

Inspector Tony Woodley

Ben's story is based on a real-life animal rescue. Could you tell us about a similar rescue you were a part of?

I was involved in the rescue of a sheep from a flooded river near Exeter. I was able to rescue it with the help of the local beach lifeguard team as the Fire Brigade were on strike. Both the lifeguard and I received an RSPCA medal for animal rescue bravery.

How do you prepare for a flood rescue?

You are normally working as part of a team

of flood-trained officers. The safety of yourself and the team is of utmost importance. Once you get to the site you carry out a risk assessment and then work out the best way to help the animals. You have lots of equipment like a dry suit, a helmet, a buoyancy aid to keep you afloat, rope to hold on to when you're in the water so you can pull yourself back to dry land, boats, etc.

Why did you want to become an RSPCA Inspector?
I had worked with animals and people for many years but also have an interest in the law. The unique role of the RSPCA Inspector was one I had wanted to get into and I was delighted that I managed to successfully apply as I know it is very competitive.

Could you describe what a typical day is like for an RSPCA Inspector?

No day is the same for an RSPCA officer. You never quite know what to expect on the next call you attend. You could be rescuing animals from danger or investigating complaints about animals not being cared for properly. The role is all about working with people to ensure the wellbeing of animals.

What is the best thing about being an RPSCA Inspector?

The best thing is getting home at the end of the day and knowing that you have improved the lives of animals either by rescuing them from danger or by advising an owner how to look after their animal or even by acting to prevent an animal being cruelly treated any more.

Some tips for looking after your animal in a flood

- Bring all small animals inside and, if possible, upstairs.

- Move food, bedding and fresh water somewhere dry.

- Keep your pet's favourite toys dry. These may comfort your pet if you have to take them somewhere else.

- If you see a farm animal in a flood, tell an adult. Do not put your own life or another life in danger to attempt an animal rescue.

- If you are concerned about the welfare of an animal, ask an adult to call the RSPCA for help. Their qualified inspectors are trained to rescue animals in distress.

Five Facts About Sheep

- Sheep usually give birth once a year and have one to three lambs. Even though some ewes have single lambs or triplets, twins are the most common.

- A lamb drinks its mother's milk for about four months and then it eats grass, hay and grain.

- Lambs can identify their mother by her bleat.

- A group of sheep is known as a flock.

- Sheep are able to see behind themselves without having to turn their head.

Take a sneak peek at the first chapter of another exciting real-life animal rescue!

1

"Hello, Pickle!" It was Friday afternoon,
and nine-year-old Emily Wilson had run
straight out of school and down the drive
to the gates. There was her gorgeous
spaniel puppy waiting for her, his feathery
white tail beating with delight, his huge
brown eyes round and bright as he saw
her coming.

Woof! he went, tugging at the lead as
if he just couldn't wait another second to
be with her. *Woof, woof!*

Dumping her school bag on the grass,
Emily crouched down and threw

her arms around her puppy, making
an enormous fuss of him. She cuddled
him and fluffed up his soft brown and
white fur and scratched him behind his
long silky ears. Pickle, meanwhile, kept
licking her face, his wet black nose cold
against her cheek, his tail wagging even
faster. He really was the cutest puppy
ever, and her best friend in the whole
world.

"Hello to you too, Em," came Mum's amused voice, and Emily looked up with a smile to see her there with Jack, Emily's brother, who was five.

"Hi, Mum. Hi, Jack," Emily said, getting up and hugging her mum. "Can I take Pickle's lead now?"

"Of course," Mum said. "I thought we could go to Albany Woods for a walk."

"Yay!" cheered Jack, and Pickle immediately started barking and leaping around at the word "walk" as if he agreed.

Emily grinned. "You know what *that* word means, don't you?" She laughed, reaching down to pat his side. "Your favourite word of all!"

"I think he's learned some new favourite words today," Mum said as they set off down the road. "Cheese straws."

Pickle woofed immediately.

"What do you mean?" asked Emily.

"I baked some cheese straws this afternoon," Mum explained, "and had just left them cooling on the table when the doorbell rang. . ."

"Uh-oh." Emily laughed. She had a pretty good idea of how this story might go.

"And guess who scrambled up to the table while I went to answer the door . . . and ate *four* of them?" Mum finished.

Pickle gave another woof as if he were proudly saying, *Me! I did it!* That's *how clever I am!* and Emily giggled. "Pickle by name, pickle by nature," she said affectionately, watching as he stopped to sniff a lamp post.

Jack looked worried. "Are there any cheese straws left?" he asked.

Mum ruffled his hair. "There are plenty left," she said, "and they're safely in a tin now, well out of reach of greedy pups. Apart from these two, which I brought along just in case there are any hungry children. . ."

"Me!" cried Jack at once.

"Thanks, Mum," said Emily, munching hers. She gave the lead a gentle tug. "Come on, Pickle, enough sniffing." He was so inquisitive that he liked to stop and smell *everything*: a nettle, the wall, a piece of litter. . . He'd often swerve right in front of Emily's legs to get to a particularly exciting gateway or hedge, and had nearly tripped her up several times in his eagerness.

Emily didn't mind. Pickle was so funny and lovely, she could forgive him anything. Ever since she'd first seen him, when they'd gone to the rehoming centre on her ninth birthday, she had been totally smitten. Back then, he'd been no more than a handful of brown and white fur with a soft round tummy and a fluffy tail. Emily's heart had simply melted when he'd gambolled over to her with a little yip of excitement, his big round eyes shining. "This one's my favourite," she'd said, reaching down to scoop him up. "Look, Mum!"

"I think he's chosen you, too," Mum had said laughing as Pickle poked out a teeny pink tongue and licked Emily's cheek.

They'd had to wait eight weeks – the longest eight weeks of Emily's life! – before the puppies were old enough to leave their mum, a sweet-natured rescue dog who was going to a new home, too. At last Emily had been able to collect Pickle, and he'd quickly become part of the family. He was nearly six months old now, and his tiny, stumpy legs had grown longer, as had his feathery tail. Emily could hardly remember what life had been like before he'd come to live with them. Having Pickle made everything much more fun, that was for sure.

"Good boy," Emily said encouragingly as he trotted along beside her. "That's it – heel!"

She and Dad had just started taking Pickle to puppy training classes, and she was trying to teach him different commands. He'd been to two lessons so far, although both had been a bit of a disaster. During the first one, Pickle had just wanted to play with all the other puppies. He was such a friendly little dog, he had kept scampering up to them whenever he'd had the chance, sniffing them and cheerfully waving his tail as if to say hello. He'd also done quite a lot of excited barking. Oh yes, and then he'd weed on the floor right at the end. . .

Luckily, the training lady had just smiled. "I've seen it all before," she'd said, passing Dad a mop. "And let's face it . . . it could have been worse."

So far Pickle had learned to sit (with a bit of help – you had to push his bottom down to remind him), and stay (for about five whole seconds) and walk to heel. Recently, Emily had tried to teach him to get into his basket, too, although he tended to jump in and then jump straight out again, his tail wagging proudly as if to say, *There – I did it. What game shall we play now?*

Once they reached the woods, Emily unclipped Pickle's lead. She could always feel him trembling with excitement whenever she let him off it. As soon as he was free this time, he gave a big happy woof and bounded down the track, his floppy ears flying out to the sides like furry brown wings. He sniffed at every tree, put his head down a rabbit hole and nosed eagerly through the long grass like an intrepid explorer on an expedition.

Emily and Jack ran beside him while Mum walked behind with their school bags. Now that Pickle's legs were longer, he could go quite fast, especially when he saw a squirrel up ahead on the path. Barking non-stop, he charged breathlessly towards the creature – which promptly shot straight up the nearest tree, its bushy tail twitching.

Emily laughed. "Oh, Pickle," she said, as he put his front paws against the tree trunk and yapped a great long message to the squirrel. "Come on," she called, "leave the poor thing alone."

It was a sunny spring day and the dappled light shone between the leafy branches of the trees. Daffodils bobbed their heads in a breeze, and the air felt warm against Emily's face. Mum suggested that they go further into the woods than usual as it was such a lovely day, and everyone – especially Pickle – thought that this was a very good idea.

They rounded the corner, and Emily saw that one of the large natural ponds in this part of the wood was covered with bright green duckweed. Pickle noticed it too, and rushed off to investigate. Unfortunately, he seemed to think the green duckweed was ordinary grass and ran cheerfully on to it . . . and in the very next moment, the "grass" gave way and he splashed straight into the water!

Emily gasped. "Pickle!" she cried, rushing over at once. The little puppy gave a yip of surprise as he found himself in the cold pond, and had to paddle his front paws to keep afloat. He was probably wondering how the grass had turned into water.

"He's swimming," Jack shouted, laughing. "Keep going, Pickle, you might get your five-metre badge!"

Emily laughed too. Pickle seemed to be rather enjoying himself, now that he'd got over the shock of cold water, and was swimming around very splashily. "Come on, boy, over here," she called, bending over a little and patting her thighs encouragingly. "Come to me, that's it."

She reached out her hand and as soon as he'd paddled near enough, she grabbed his collar and hauled him out of the water.

Covered with duckweed and mud, Pickle looked completely bedraggled. He smelled absolutely terrible, too.

"Pickle Wilson, what are you like?" Emily groaned. "Look at him, Mum."

"Poo!" Jack said, holding his nose. "Pickle pongs."

"It's not his fault," Emily said loyally. "Is it, boy? He. . . Aargh!" She leaped back as Pickle chose that very moment to give himself a thorough shake, spraying Emily with stinky mud from head to foot.

"Yuck!" she shrieked, wiping a strand of duckweed from her face. Pickle wagged his tail as if he'd just been very helpful, and Emily found herself giggling. You really couldn't be cross with a puppy like Pickle!

Jack burst out laughing, and Mum looked as if she was trying not to chuckle too. "Oh dear," she said. "What a mucky pup – and what a mucky daughter! I hope you two won't get too cold now you're so wet. Perhaps we'd better head back."

Emily agreed. "Let's put you on the lead, Pickle," she said, clipping it safely on to his collar. "I think that's enough exploring for one day, don't you? We don't want you getting into another pickle!"

Woof! Pickle agreed, wagging his muddy tail.

They set off towards home, Pickle's fur slowly drying in the sunshine. As they passed their neighbours' house they saw that Mr and Mrs Turner were in their front garden, pulling up some weeds.

Mr Turner looked up and smiled when he saw them. "Goodness me, Pickle, what *have* you been up to?" he asked.

Mrs Turner's eyes twinkled. "It looks like somebody will be going straight into the bath when you get home," she said, laughing.

Mum shook her head. "I'm tempted to put the pair of them in together," she joked. "I'm not sure who's the muddiest, Emily or the dog!"

Once they were back inside, Emily quickly changed out of her muddy clothes and helped Mum fill the bath for Pickle, who wasn't very happy about being washed at all. Despite Emily's best

efforts, he kept trying to clamber out, his claws uselessly scrabbling at the side. Water and the bubbles from his special doggy shampoo went *everywhere*, and soon Emily and Mum were drenched, too.

Afterwards, Emily dried Pickle in a big fluffy towel and brushed the tangles out of his fur. "There," she said when it shone once more. "You're as good as new."

Once Pickle had eaten his tea, he seemed so tired that he barely had the energy to move. Instead of making the short journey to his basket, he curled up on the floor by his food bowl and closed his eyes.

Emily smiled as his head sank dreamily on to his front paws. "Pickle! Get in your basket." she reminded him in the sing-song voice she always tried to use when giving him commands.

Pickle opened one eye and peered groggily at her.

"Good boy, Pickle, get in your basket," Emily coaxed.

Pickle was so sleepy he could hardly walk, but he obediently staggered to his feet and trotted over to his basket. He flopped into it, gave a deep sigh of relief, tucked his nose under his favourite cuddly bear, then promptly fell straight back to sleep. Within seconds he was snoring.

Emily stroked his soft fur. "What a good boy," she told him, gently resting her head on his sleeping body and listening to his heartbeat. "I hope you have a lovely dream about chasing squirrels. Sleep well . . . and let's have another adventure tomorrow."

Buy the book to read the rest of the story!

Collect the whole series...

Based on a real-life animal rescue

RSPCA

Little Lost Hedgehog

Buying this book helps the RSPCA save animals' lives

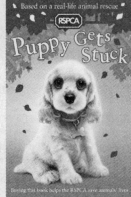

Based on a real-life animal rescue

RSPCA

Puppy Gets Stuck

Buying this book helps the RSPCA save animals' lives

Based on a real-life animal rescue

RSPCA

Lamb All Alone

Buying this book helps the RSPCA save animals' lives

Based on a real-life animal rescue

RSPCA

The Abandoned Kitten

Buying this book helps the RSPCA save animals' lives

Coming in
May 2013

Based on a real-life animal rescue

RSPCA

Little Owl Needs a Home

Buying this book helps the RSPCA save animals' lives

Coming in
October 2013

Join the RSPCA!

You'll receive:

- **six issues of *animal action* magazine**
- **a brilliant welcome pack**
- **a FAB joining gift**
- **and a FREE gift with every issue.**

Go to: **www.rspca.org.uk/ theclub**

Ask an adult to call: **0300 123 0346** and pay by debit/credit card.

ALL FOR £15!
(£22 OVERSEAS)

RSPCA, Wilberforce Way, Southwater, Horsham, West Sussex RH13 9RS
The RSPCA helps animals in England and Wales. Registered charity no. 219099

For more information on the Animal Action Club check out: www.rspca.org.uk/theden

You'll also love...

Packed with cute stickers and fun facts!